SCAVENGER

A Primal Approach To Lifestyle Change

Donny Dust

To my tribe.

SCAVENGER

Scavengers play an important role in the ecosystem by consuming the dead animal and plant material.

Scavenging is both a carnivorous and an herbivorous feeding behavior in which the scavenger feeds on dead animal and plant material present in its habitat.

Early versions of man were considered scavengers before they were hunters and gatherers.

A person's or the entire tribe's existence could be based on their ability to scavenge sources of food from predatory kills.

CONTENTS

Chapter 1

DEATH'S INTRO

Sorry to ruin your day, but you're going to die. Maybe not today, maybe not tomorrow, but one day you will die. We all will. Life keeps just one promise — death. Death is guaranteed. We all share death no matter what our race, sexual preference, religion, economic standing or politics. Some people fear death to the extent that discussing it or even thinking about it will cause debilitating depression, anxiety and stress. People all around the world believe there is a divine action after this life. People can't fathom their existence without having an aspect of continuation or life after death. *I know there is something after this current life,* they proclaim when they are challenged or questioned. *How can our existence now, be the only existence we have?*

To overcome that stress and fear of the unknown, societies and cultures for thousands of years have developed different "death theories" — theories consisting of a life-after-death scenario are the most popular. Other theories like reincarnation, living as ghosts in a parallel dimension, ascending into some ethereal plan, judgment and damnation, drinking beer forever with your bros in a majestic beer hall or that our consciousness will carry on forever in the machines that will one day rule the world. Turn on the TV or pick up a book and you can find stories, myths and legends of people attempting to beat death and live forever. From historical to modern cultures, this has been an obsession, but the finality of death is a reality that all living things share.

One possibility (and I think it's the most logical) in death is that we have no idea what happens and really *anything* is possible. That was my outlook before one cold February morning in 2017 when my outlook on death and my entire world was turned upside down.

Let me begin with why having a massive heart attack at the age of 37 was the best thing that could have happened to me and the people around me. I know, shocking isn't it? But let's start at the beginning — well, not all the way to the very beginning, but just that day when my story began. That's a good starting point and I'll be sure to toss in some background information through this first bit to get you up to speed. Let's go!

Chapter 2

BEFORE

February 2, 2017, 9:30 a.m.

"The word is, Scavenger."

"Scavenger . . . Sca . . . ven . . . ger" she said quietly under her breath and with panic.

"Scavenger . . . May I have the word in a sentence please?"

"Vultures are considered to be scavenger birds."

A slight look of disappointment showed on the uniformed, pigtailed, fifth-grade girl's face as she obviously did not prepare for this word during her weeks of spelling bee preparation. Ten other kids who were also participating in the fifth-grade spelling bee stood along the wall next to Pigtails; my son, who knew this word for sure was to the right of Pigtails, followed by four others who were all smiling indicating they knew how to spell it, but one was actually smiling and making faces at his buddie who had missed his word two rounds before. Two other students looked relieved that it wasn't their word, while another two looked pissed as all hell because their mom or dad made them participate in the fifth-grade spelling bee. The last student really had no idea what was going on as his index finger aggressively tickled his brain in front of the class. Maybe he was searching for the answer up there. Who knows, but he was knuckle deep in his left nostril.

I thought to myself, *Pigtails has to have one of those Moms who more than likely told her, "You will win no matter what! Everyone's a winner. If you study hard, have courage in your heart and give it your best, you will never lose."* Mom probably even gave her a sappy, total bullshit story about how she overcame her fears when she was her age because her goal was to win her fifth-grade spelling bee and she did just that. I can't stand goal makers. I literally want to punch myself in the face when I hear people talk about goal setting . . . but I digress.

My son, who was standing next to Pigtails, smiled because he knew the correct spelling of the word and if Pigtails missed it, the word would pass to him. I told my son during his three days of preparation, "If you want to win, you have to spell all the words given to you correctly and spelling the words correctly is the only, surefire, way to win a spelling bee." Spell every damn word correctly and he had it made. Unlike Pigtails' mom, I didn't have a story to share about spelling bee success. I suck at spelling. As a 37-year-old husband and father of two sons, I rely heavily on spell check and praise its existence today.

"May I have the definition of the word please?" She looked up timidly towards the teacher administering the words and then at her mom, who gave her a reassuring look of encouragement. Keep in mind that this is a 5th-grade spelling bee and the rules were very serious so serious parents had to sign an acknowledgment of the rules: No clapping until a winner is identified, no talking, no grunting, no speaking, no sounds, no hand gestures, no sudden movements, no photos, no videos, no live streams, no facial expressions of any type . . . but have fun. Parents could pretty much mouth breathe and stand motionless.

"Scavenger: a person who searches for and collects discarded items or an animal that feeds on carrion, dead plant material or refuse."

I thought to myself, *I hope Pigtails screws this one up as my boy knows this word. He has heard me say it hundreds of times. Come on, you don't know it! Mess it up!* I know that is something I should not be thinking to myself, but my kid has this one for sure.

"Scavenger . . . S-C-A-V- . . . ."

Don't say 'E' Pigtails, say 'A.' I know you're thinking 'A' so say 'A.' Don't say 'E.' I know you think it's an 'A,' so say 'A'! Say 'A' and let my son have this one. Don't say 'E'! I say in my mind over and over again, hoping to hear Pigtails sweet little voice say "A". I pick my head up slowly and lock eyes with my son, just for a moment as we both know that he has this word in the bag.

"S-C-A-V- . . . ."

That was it. That exact moment when Pigtails pulled out the remaining letters E-N-G-E-R that "IT" first hit me. It was that quick. What was "IT"? At the time I didn't know. It was a pain, an uncomfortable sensation in the center of my chest that I had never felt. I have had broken fingers, ankles, toes, teeth, elbows and ribs before, but this was not a broken bone. That can't be "IT". I have had worms, ticks, fleas, parasites, untreated and undiagnosed rashes. I went through the checklist. *Nope, don't think so. Not this time!* I have had all sorts of cuts, bruises, concussions, twists, stab wounds, sicknesses and who knows what else. I even had a vasectomy in 2009 with no anesthesia or numbing medication. I know, crazy, right? I have had dysentery so many times from drinking untreated and tainted water that I literally "shit the bed" I was so sick. One time, I ruptured my eye while playing air drums. I was drumming intensely with two ink pens in my hand and accidentally stabbed myself in the eye. When Nirvana's "Smells Like Teen Spirit" comes on, you *must* air-drum! However, this "IT" at the spelling bee was foreign, something new and unexplained. Something completely unknown to me and my long medical resume. . . . Then "IT" was gone.

As quick as Pigtails could say E-N-G-E-R the remaining letters of the word "SCAVENGER," my son followed and missed his word (a word I can't even remember to this day), and then IT was gone. Completely over with. The spelling bee was over as well. I gave my son a standard Dad high-five among the sea of moms saying "Nice job," and I informed him I would pick him up with his brother after school. He asked, "First five again?" and as he gave me the, "Can you do it?" look, I replied, "You know it!"

First five at my son's school is a badge of honor. Nobody actually gets a badge, but in my mind I'm the reigning champ with a dashboard full of badges. Simply put, first five means you're one of the First Five cars in the carpool pick up line. Carpool pickup line at my son's school can take forever and can really mess up an after-school schedule if you don't arrive early. In my personal opinion, any position past First Five and you don't love your kids. That's the truth. I make it a point to always be in the First Five at pickup. That's a lie. I really shoot to be first three. It was a daily challenge my sons always issued and a challenge always accepted.

As I slowly walked back to my car from the fifth-grade class with "IT" on my mind, I continued to run through every possible scenario of what "IT" could be. After a five-minute drive home the wannabe doctor in me concluded that since I had just arrived back from two weeks of teaching in Anchorage Alaska at sea level and because I currently live well above 7,500 feet in Monument Colorado, "IT" must be the elevation change and "IT" will require some time to adjust. But wait, the diagnosis speculation continues.

While in Anchorage, I also purchased some moose antlers that I have been meticulously grinding in my garage to turn into primitive soft percussion tools. I should add that I teach wilderness survival, primitive skills and wilderness self-reliance as a profession. So, the moose antler and my methods with it are pretty common. Continuing on, my theory was that the moose antler dust particles that were in the air caused some respiratory discomfort because I was breathing the dust particles in without wearing a mask . . . because, as everyone knows, masks are stupid. Official diagnosis: Acute Moose Particle Respiratory Elevation Adjustment Pain (AMPREAP).

After diagnosing myself with AMPREAP, I continued on with my day as if nothing had happened and, in my mind, nothing did happen. I continued to grind my moose antler, still with no mask, but I did turn my head slightly to the side to avoid breathing in too much moose antler particles. Shortly, I went out for a brief 6 mile run around my neighborhood. I should also add that, during this time I was six months away from participating in a Super Jungle Ultra Marathon that was 245 kilometers, self-supported, over ten days running, 50+ river crossings, and all taking place in Peru. So I thought, *Let's just stick to 6 miles. I don't want my AMPREAP to get worse.*

During that short 6-mile run, actually right around 5 and half miles, a slight hint of AMPREAP emerged once again. It came hard and fast this time and lasted for a few seconds. It was enough to make me stop running, throw my arms in the air and say aloud, "This elevation is going to kill me!" In hindsight, it was not the elevation that was going to kill me, but something worse. I decided to walk the remainder of my run, eventually winding up at home completely winded and exhausted.

I waited in the carpool pickup line as I normally did. Today's position in the first five: #2. My arch nemesis in the fight for first five was a 70-year-old grandmother who I called "The Pilot." She drove a Honda Pilot (hence the name) with tinted windows, ski racks and a bumper sticker that said "Coexist" (a standard bumper sticker on most Colorado vehicles). The Pilot often grabbed the #1 position and I swear up and down she made it her daily duty to beat me. She would even pretend to retrieve something out of her trunk, just so she could walk to the back and throw me a, maybe-next-time wave as I sat behind her steaming. When I did snag the #1 position, I often caught The Pilot looking in my truck as she walked by giving a "WTF" look at all the stuff inside.

My car was typically littered with animal hides, fire making materials, primitive weapons and stone tools — all the things I use in my survival and primitive living instruction. I let it go as just a curious look, peppered with a bit of judgment. When I was teaching a class in the mountains . . . or in a foreign land like Kansas or North Carolina, my truck overflowed with a bounty of weird and interesting things. Many times, upon pick up from school, my sons would find something in the backseat, hold it up and say, "What is this, Dad?" My typical response ranged from; the leg tendons of a deer, the teeth of a skunk, triggers for deadfall traps or even dried elk guts used for making bowstrings. After picking my kids up from school that day, we drove home running through the standard parental questions and child responses about their school happenings:

"How was school?"

"Fine."

"Good."

"How were your lunches?"

"Delicious."

"Yummy."

"How much homework do you guys have?"

"None."

"Some."

"How are your friends?"

"Cool."

"Ok."

"What happened at school? Anything exciting?"

"Nothing."

"This kid puked at lunch and then someone else puked because of the smell."

Yes! I'm in! Someone puked at lunch causing a chain reaction of puking. I should add that I spent a chunk of my time in the United States Marine Corps as an interrogator, so I know how to run a series of questions and "break" a detainee. Using the basic interrogatives; Who, What, Where, When, Why, What Else, What Other are key to obtain the free narrative. Interrogatives get a conversation going . . . anyway, you get my point. However, my fifth-grade and second-grade detainees were up to speed on my methods of interrogation.

Both my sons are amazingly awesome. They really are. They are both independent and have their own interests if compared to each other. There was a chunk of time during their young lives when their mother, my wife, had an elective double mastectomy because of a genetic disposition to BRCA1 (Breast Cancer 1) gene in her body, followed by their grandmother, aka "Nana," having full-blown breast cancer with all the treatments that go along with it. My sons took care of both those ladies physically, mentally and emotionally. During my wife's and Nana's recovery, I was not home. I was living in a tent in a wooded area on the east coast working for a horrible government contracting company to maintain health insurance to cover my wife's medical expenses. Those two young men I'm honored to call my sons stepped up bravely at such a young age. Now that is real courage.

After the short ride home and all the smelly, sticky and chunky details about the puking incident, my two detainees started their homework and I helped as needed. I should also add that, at the time, our house was under a serious renovation. About three weeks before I left for Alaska, the main sewer line leading into our house became clogged — Ironically perfect considering my own, as yet unknown, "clogged" state — and backed up causing black, gray and just about every color of water and waste to overflow into all our bathrooms and laundry room. While under construction, we hung out at the house to maintain normalcy for the kids, but stayed nights at Nana's house a few minutes away. Secretly, I stayed to keep an eye on the contractors and ensure stuff was getting done.

"Dad, I have to pick a book from this list for my book report. What one do you think?" my oldest son asked. He handed me a list with several different titles. I scanned the list of books and found the few books I had read as a kid. Many of the books I had never even heard of. What happened to *Call of The Wild, Last of the Mohicans, Where the Red Fern Grows* and *The Great Gatsby?*

"What one do you think?" I said handing the list back to him. "Any titles catch your interest? My son ran down the list and picked one of my favorite books.

"What about *Hatchet* by Gary Paulsen," he asked, looking at me as if knowing that was one of my favorite books of all time. "You read this when you were my age didn't you?"

"I did," I said. "It is one of my favorite books. I actually read that book several times." I continued with, "*Hatchet* is a book of adventure and courage. A book filled with one boy's challenge to survive." I could tell my son was pleased with his choice and was excited to read the story. "Alright gents, let's pack our stuff and head to Nana's. Dinner awaits!" The last contractor left and we were on our way to Nana's.

"Hey Nana! How are you?" the two detainees said in unison to their grandmother as she quickly heralded them inside from the cold February evening. Nana lived alone, but always had the kids over to her house after school and had even designated a room for them to stay in when they stayed over.

"Better now that you're here. Was the school day a good one?"

"Yes."

"Yes."

"Did you get your homework done?"

"Almost."

"Yes."

"Did you have snack?"

"Yes."

"Yes."

I recognized this line of questioning was going nowhere quickly with only direct questions by being applied by Nana. People use basic interrogatives. Avoid questions that draw out a single word response or a "Yes," or "No," answer. Do this if you need information. I quickly toss Nana a bone and shout that my youngest should tell Nana about the chain reaction puking incident at lunchtime. My youngest quickly dropped his personal effects and began to regale her with all the details.

After my son was done with his theatrical version of the "lunchtime puke chain reaction" to Nana, we had a quick conversation about the upcoming days and the upcoming week. Nana and I shared kid duties, but when I was in the backcountry or mountains teaching, she was 100% on duty and she loved it. Nana moved from Massachusetts and followed us to Colorado as my wife is her only child and my two sons are her only grandchildren.

A short time later, my wife arrived at Nana's from work. I should add that my wife is smoking hot. That's all. In all reality, my wife works in Denver for an education tech company and commutes hours a day to get to from work. She works hard and has to deal with all levels of chaos at her place of work. I like to have meals, household duties and kid-specific stuff done for her when she arrives. I like her to be able to come home, relax and hang with the family with no extra duties to be done. I can't do this all the time, especially if I'm teaching or traveling, but it happens when I can make it happen. She knows I get a joy from it, but she also knows that I need to run barefoot through the mountains frequently to maintain my social sanity.

Once dinner was concluded and dishes were addressed, a wrestling match commenced on Nana's living room floor between the detainees and me — an all-out prison riot. That's when "IT" . . . excuse me, my AMPREAP decided to show its ugly face again. Same pain, the same foreign discomfort, creeped back into the center of my chest. This time my AMPREAP was extremely intense. It was so bad I had to pause and grab at my chest for a second. I excused myself from the prison riot that was happening and slimmed my way onto Nana's couch. However, it came and left quickly — just a few seconds, maybe one and half seconds. Say the word "chest" and that's how long it lasted. My wife was keen to my removal from the wrestling match and asked the boys to give me a second and sent them to go get ready for bed.

"Are you alright?" she asked. "It looks like you're in some type of pain," she said.

"I think it's your mother's cooking," I said jokingly. "Just a little acid reflux. No big deal," I told her.

As the two detainees walked to their cell blocks, I chatted with my wife. I should add that my wife is the most amazing thing that has ever happened to me.

She really is. We actually met in Hawaii when she was "studying abroad" and I was stationed there for my first duty station. We met at the Rodeo Cantina in the Aloha Towers on Taco Tuesday. For a single Marine and his buddies, one-dollar tacos and two-dollar Coronas are a great deal that can't be passed up. It was also easy pickings for young marines as we all knew it would be flooded with drunk college girls, desperate female tourists hoping to fulfill that Hawaiian romance fantasy and the occasional local lady. The odds were in our favor. Long story short, my smoking-hot wife and I locked eyes, she sauntered over and started flirting. Followed by all types of non-verbal body language indicating that she wanted a drink. You know the signs: empty hands, eye contact with your drink, licking lips, scanning the drink menu — all textbook signs. I was well aware of the drink scams some ladies conducted back then, but after some conversation mixed with some Bon Jovi lyrics to test the waters (I used song lyrics from Bon Jovi to woo the ladies) and some straight love-at-first-sight type feelings, I bought my future wife a drink.

Back at Nana's, after my wife shared the details of her day, I gave her the outcome of mine. The spelling bee, Pigtails, the knuckle-deep brain tickler, my moose grinding, my 6-mile run, First Five, The Pilot, the puking chain reaction, Hatchet and the status of the house. My wife and I read the kids a story, tucked them in and retreated to our designated room in Nana's house. We discussed our plans for our youngest son's birthday that was nine days away. The big 7 was coming up fast for him and we had some great things planned. We also discussed the renovations on the house; what insurance was going to cover, what we had to cover and overall progress. I kissed her gently and watched her read a book on her iPhone as I feel asleep.

Chapter 3

DURING

February 3, 2017, 2:30 a.m.

"Something is wrong," I said as I reached to grab some part of my wife in an attempt to wake her.

"Eliza, something isn't right."

"Eliza . . . ."

I ran to the toilet and began to let loose everything and anything that was in my body, but nothing comes out. I fall back onto the bathroom floor and begin writhing in immense agony on the floor. My chest felt like it was on fire. I can recall the exact feeling. Imagine someone taking hot coals and placing them on your chest, then strapping you to a table so can't move. You can't shake them or brush them away. They just burn straight through. That was the burning I felt. That was a burning sensation like nothing I had ever experienced.

"Donny? Are you okay?" my wife asked with panic in her heart, but grit in her voice.

"Something is wrong. My chest is on fire . . . It hurts! . . . It hurts so bad!" I moaned "Eliza, you have to help me."

"I'm coming in."

My wife who was standing on the other side of the bathroom door pushed her way in and helped me to my feet. She looked at me in the light and knew immediately something was wrong and I could also see on her face that something was scaring her. We walked arm-in-arm down the stairs to the kitchen. She sat me in a chair, grabbed some baby aspirin, slammed them down my throat and woke Nana. For the first time in a long time, I became scared. I became scared when my wife said the words, "heart attack." I remember it exactly. She looked at Nana and then down at me propped up in a chair like a rag doll and says, "Donny, we need to get you to the hospital because you're having a heart attack."

I'll be 100% honest. I was scared. When I heard the words "heart attack." I did not believe it . . . but I was scared. Call it blind ignorance, but in my mind, I was too young to have a heart attack. I have been in some scary situations; combat overseas, sketchy as all hell rock climbing trips, predatory animal encounters, avalanches, car crashes, fights, Class-5 white water rafting on an inflatable kayak, helicopter crashes, having guns pulled on me, having knives pulled on me, but they were all nothing compared to when my wife said, "You are having a heart attack."

During the 15-minute drive to the emergency room that consisted of me telling my wife to slow down because cops are out, and we don't need a ticket right now and trying to convince her to stop for a quick Gatorade as I was dying of thirst, my AMPREAP was coming and going like a pregnant woman having labor contractions. In between my AMPREAP contractions, I finally brought my wife up to speed on my AMPREAP diagnosis and at the time, I believed that's what "IT" really was. Not a heart attack. I even recall thinking I was 99% sure it was AMPREAP. Thousands of men die every year from stupidity and I was well on my way to becoming part of that statistic.

Once we arrived at the emergency room, my memory of the events fades in and out, but I have a good grasp of what happened. First, I walked through the giant rotating door of the hospital only to be directed to a metal detector that signaled I was carrying something I shouldn't. Keep in mind, once my wife hit the rotating door she was off like a jackrabbit to the emergency room counter to get help and inform the staff of my AMPREAP. The security guard said, "No weapons allowed." Please empty your pockets." The security guard confiscated my small pocket knife and directed me to fill out a Personal Items Receipt form and I could pick up my knife when I left the building.

I grabbed the clipboard to fill out the paperwork, but my wife grabbed me quickly by the arm saying, "Leave it." I lost that battle.

My wife yelled for a hospital staff member to hurry up with the wheelchair and they came running. They lost that battle. I argued about being put in a wheelchair and said I was fine to walk. I lost that battle as well. I made the on-call doctor and several nurses laugh at my AMPREAP diagnosis. That pissed me off as I knew that was more than likely the issue. I eventually lost that battle as well. I took two massive doses of morphine that I think did nothing, but might explain why I can't remember much. I think I lost that battle too. I do remember being wheeled into a well-lit room with tons of monitors and I remember kissing my wife one last time before going in. One more battle lost.

"Mr. Dust? Welcome back." the short, maybe early 30's, female doctor said. "You suffered a massive heart attack. A LAD heart attack. Your LAD, or left anterior descending artery was 99% blocked. You should be dead."

"What?! No way!" I said.

" A LAD heart attack is known as the widow-maker heart attack and has the highest death risk."

"Wait, hold on," I said. "Are you telling me I had a heart attack? I'm only 37 years old." I say in a pissed, yet shocked way. This same moment, I see my wife once again for the first time after coming to my wits. It was like the same moment I had had before almost 15 years before on a Taco Tuesday in Honolulu, Hawaii. I was excited, nervous and knew it was love at first sight once again . . . and it has been that way every day since. I see her, and finally everything the doctor says starts to become fully true, but I try one last time. "Doc, . . . are you sure? I was grinding some moose antler and . . . ."

"Mr. Dust, your wife informed me of your moose antler altitude theory and—"

" I call it AMPREAP or Acute Moose Particle Respiratory Elevation Adjustment Pain."

"Sure thing," she says, "but, as a Cardiologist, I can guarantee that you had a heart attack."

"Ok . . . sounds like a sure thing," I say with final acceptance.

"It's a big thing, Donny," my wife says. "People die from this."

"Your wife is absolutely correct, Mr. Dust, people die all the time from this." The doctor continued, "The heart is a muscle and needs a constant supply of blood. When something cuts the blood supply off, you have a heart attack. Your left anterior descending artery or your LAD is the major pipeline for carrying blood to the heart. If the LAD gets 100% blocked, it's almost certain death." My eyes widen in complete disbelief. "Your LAD, Mr. Dust, was 99% blocked. A very critical blockage."

"What caused this?" I soberly asked.

"Great question and for most people it's lifestyle choices. Things like smoking, an unhealthy diet full of saturated fats and cholesterol." She continued with, "Lack of exercise, drinking, uncontrolled diabetes, obesity, can cause this, but in your case, Mr. Dust. . . . it's genetics."

"What? . . . Genetics? Seriously? My genes caused this?"

"I'm sorry to say so, Mr. Dust, but, yes. A person who has a family history of cardiac disorders is highly prone to heart attack. You are that person." I took it all in — all and any information the doctor had to offer. At that moment, I knew it was serious. The doctor explained that she had placed a catheter in my wrist and repaired the ruptured artery with a stent. She continued explaining that I was going to be on a cardiac recovery plan that could take several months, I was going to be on a pill regimen for some time, probably my entire life; and my life, actions and behaviors would need some major adjustment. Once again, I'm extremely lucky to be alive.

Beep . . . beep . . . beep . . . beep . . . beep . . . beep . . . beep . . . beep . . . beep.

"What the hell?" I said, sitting up in my bed as my heart monitor made a boring melody of my beating heart. I was moved to a private room with a dedicated on-call nurse standing by around the clock. The clock on the wall told me it was 1:15 a.m. I thought to myself it hasn't even been 24 hours since I had hot coals dropped my chest, had my knife confiscated and my AMPREAP diagnosis was mocked by the on-call doctor in the emergency room. "I can't believe this," I said quietly, ensuring not to wake my wife up who was sleeping on one of those kinky plastic futuristic hospital recliner bed chairs. You all know the type I'm talking about. The ones that look like a weird sex chair from the 60's. Don't Play dumb.

"God damn, Donny!" I said, still sitting up. "What the fuck did you do?" I started to think about my entire life and all the dumb shit I had done that could have caused this, all the days that I could have worked out an extra ten minutes to prevent this and all the time I could have missed because of this. "Doc said it was genetics, but that can't be the only thing." Then I started to think about my wife and sons and how this; my life, my own existence could have ended less than 24 hours ago.

The clock on the wall now displayed the time: 2:05 a.m. "I Could have died in my sleep!" I felt horrible thinking that, after my sons went to bed that night dreaming the dreams of a nine and six-year-old, they would have woken up to a dead father. I felt ashamed that my youngest son's birthday would always be associated with my death for the rest of his life. I felt embarrassed that my children would grow up without a father. I felt disgusted about how selfish I was and how my own neglect could have harmed my son's mental and personal wellbeing. I could have stripped away their innocence and abandoned them in a world where fathers are needed more than ever. *Coward!* I said to myself, shaking my head in complete shame.

My wife slowly adjusted her body in the plastic hospital recliner and I could see she was uncomfortable. I felt like waking her and giving her my hospital bed, but I knew I would lose that battle. "I'm sorry, Eliza," I said, "I let you down." I cried a few tears of complete shame thinking that the one person I would do anything for, the one person that I would give my life to without hesitation, I let down. My wife has been and will always be my best friend. I can't imagine not being there for her. *Fucking coward!* I said again, disgusted with my current situation. What kind of man would leave his wife like that? What kind of man would do this to his family?

I shed a few more tears thinking that my wife — the girl I saw instantly when I walked into the Rodeo Cantina that night, the girl I so desperately wanted to go talk to, but was afraid to because she was so beautiful, so perfect that I knew I never stood a chance — would be all alone. I felt ashamed that when my wife, my world, my everything kissed her husband goodnight, she would find him dead in the morning. A few more tears fell as I covered my face in shame only to come to the truth of how lucky I really am.

Chapter 4

AFTER

2:40 a.m. *It's been 24 hours and ten minutes since my heart attack,* I thought. *Well . . . now what?* I asked myself, looking around the room as if the answer might be hiding next to the rubber surgical gloves. At the same moment, a lovely on-call nurse appeared, standing directly next to me to take my vitals.

"I didn't see you come in," I said curiously. "You appeared out of nowhere".

"Sorry to startle you. Can't sleep can ya?" she said as she began to slide the blood pressure cuff up my arm. "I'll just be a minute."

"No. I can't at the moment. A lot on my mind. I'm sure I'll doze off soon," I said.

"I can give you something to help you sleep," she whispered.

"No more pills," I said in desperation. I did not recognize this on-call nurse. The nurse changeover happened when I was awake. The outgoing nurse introduced me to the incoming nurse and this nurse was neither one of them. "You want to know something crazy?" I asked.

"What's that?" she said, followed by "100 over 70" as she softly announced my blood pressure to the room with a slight head bob saying, "Nice job."

"Yesterday at this time, my wife was flying down the highway to get me to this emergency room because I was having a heart attack." I explained this as if she was not aware of why I was in the cardiac recovery wing. "It could have been game over me," I said.

"You are very lucky" said the nurse. "Not everyone makes it. You are considerably younger than 99% of the heart attack victims I see. You beat death," she said, as if I went 12 rounds with death himself. "I bet people could learn a lot from you."

I looked at the nurse and thought, *She has a good point. People could learn from my pain.* I thought she must see people twice as old as me and I should feel lucky. "Have you ever had anyone in their thirties before?"

"Open up," she said, as she placed an electronic thermometer in my mouth. "I'm new to this hospital, just filling in for a bit, but you're the only person under forty I have ever met or treated that has had a heart attack. I do know that the hospital treated a young man in his late 20's around Christmas of last year. He beat death as well," she said with a subtle smile, "just like you."

"Taattsss razzy" I said, with the thermometer still in my mouth.

"It is," she replied, as if she completely knew the language of thermometer talk. "More and more people these days are treated for cardiovascular disease, it's not good. 98.3 degrees. Nice temp. That's good," she smiled. "I think people could learn from you, Mr. Dust," she said, writing the temp down on a piece of paper presumably to add to my chart later. "Make sure when you get out of here you take the time to recover and help people," she said with a sweet, but serious tone. "Having been so close to death, people can learn from your pain."

"Will do," I said. "Thanks. I appreciate you."

The on-call nurse smiled and revealed that next time I wake up, she'll be gone. She explained her shift will have ended and there will be another on-call nurse on duty. Still, to this day, I can't remember her name or her face clearly. That quick conversation, in the darkness of my hospital room, with my wife asleep on a kinky-looking plastic hospital recliner bed gave me peace in my heart because just moments before I was in a dark place; feeling shame, guilt, loneliness and anger. Thank you my mysterious nighttime on-call nurse. Thank you, wherever you are.

February 4, 2017, 10:30 a.m.

"Donny . . . Donny wake up for a minute, someone is here to see you," my wife said, gently pulling me out of sleep.

"What? . . . Oh . . . Hey, brother, how goes it? My eyes slowly came into focus as my friend Rick stood with a look of disbelief on his face.

"Dude? . . . What the heck happened?" Rick, who was ten years my senior was more than just a friend. He was a mentor to me in many ways. Rick is a hard-as-nails retired Army Jumpmaster and I had the pleasure of working with him. Let me put it to you like this, Rick went into the Army at 6"0 and retired at just over 5'9. He had done so many jumps his spine was compressed and he lost height. He is still waiting for the V.A. to pull their head out of their ass.

Our families got along nicely as we had sons of similar ages and wives that were good friends as well. We went on camping trips together, had family get-togethers and were close. One early March, Rick and I brought our kids camping in the mountains and we were obliterated by a major freak springtime snowstorm. His truck lacked four-wheel drive and couldn't make it through the snow. (I still bust his balls about it.) I pulled him for 12 miles through three feet of snow, down a winding mountain road only to get trapped in a small town for two days as the pass to get out was snowed in. Rick, his son, my two boys and myself had a blast; our wives were pissed! It was a great time.

"Bit of a blockage in the old ticker," I said with a smile. "Show him the photo Eliza." I gestured to my wife to supply Rick with the photo the doctor took when I was under. "Check it out. That's where my artery was and, as you can see, it exploded."

"Donny, this isn't funny," my wife said as she showed Rick a photo of the exploded LAD on my heart.

"Go big or go home," I said jokingly. I continue with, "Marines . . . we are always getting issued shitty gear," as I point to my heart. Rick smiles slightly as my wife shoots him a don't-encourage-him glare.

"I can't believe you had a heart attack. As a matter of fact, nobody believes me when I tell them," Rick said. "I'm glad you're alright." Rick looked in my wife's direction, "Eliza, if you need anything let me know. I assume this guy will be out of commission for some time," gesturing to me.

"Thanks, Rick, I appreciate it," my wife said.

"Don't worry about it, man. I'll be back on my feet, running through the mountains doing my thing before you know it," I say, with a confident smile.

"Seriously, Donny, don't rush anything. Please make sure you're fully recovered and are okay before you get back into the bush," Rick said, with some genuine worry in his voice. "Everybody is shocked at what happened and going out and getting checked. You scared them."

"Tell you what, Rick, if I have to be the example to all the smokers, overweight and just unhealthy people out there, I don't mind that. Shit, I don't mind being an example to everyone if this is what it takes. Let people learn from me."

Rick and I shot the shit for a while longer, before my new on-call nurse came into my room to check my vitals and declared I needed to rest. *Yes, Mein*

Fuhrer, I thought to myself. I liked my mysterious on-call nurse from the night before much better. I asked Rick to let people know that I was OK and not to worry. I asked him to go out and get checked before what happened to me happens to him.

Let me bring this entire thing into focus: just turned 37, fit enough to conduct a Super Jungle Ultra Marathon, I don't smoke, eat clean, barely drink, maintain a lifestyle that is far more active than the majority of the population, consider myself to be a modern-day hunter, gatherer, scavenger; I have an extremely healthy marriage, healthy family, no family history and I have a heart attack. How can this be?

Now, let me be the first to tell you that the majority of the signs and symptoms someone is supposed to have when a heart attack is near, I didn't. I had no radiating pain down my arm. My back, jaw and neck had no pain, were not tight, had no pressure and no aching. I was not dizzy or lightheaded. I was not fatigued, nor did I have any cold sweats or hot sweats. All I had was major chest pain and dry heaving. I, like most people, believed the pain in the arm symptom to be the most frequent indication, but all I can say is, *everyone is different*. Listen to your body!

Cardiac rehabilitation is a mandated recovery program that all heart attack patients partake in. Cardiac rehabilitation was six weeks long; every Monday,

Wednesday and Friday. It was quick, regimented and easy to accomplish when that was all you had to do. It also encompassed nutrition classes, stress and depression classes, medication classes and heart attack information classes. Leaving cardiac rehabilitation I had to: live and eat in a heart-healthy lifestyle . . . check! Stay active and keep cardiovascular strong . . . check! Take my medications . . . check! Keep positive and motivated . . . check! Maintain a stress-free lifestyle . . . check! You might be thinking that the recovery process sounds easy, but, I can assure you, I'm an outlier among most heart attack survivors. Some cardiac related patients who attend cardiac-rehab are there for several weeks to even months. In the simplest answer, I spent less time in recovery because I'm younger than 99.4% percent of the cardiac rehabilitation attendees and, prior to my heart attack, I was in excellent health. However, being the youngest, I came to a quick realization that might seem a little dark to most, but it's the truth. Follow along if you can.

Let's take a 75-year-old man who has a heart attack. Two outcomes can happen; one he dies from the heart attack or two he makes it through and he goes on living his life until he is 85 or 90 and eventually dies from old age. So we can determine he had about 15 years of life after his attack. Now let's take me. I have a heart attack at 37, recover properly and I could live to a ripe old age of 85 or 90 years. We can determine that I have about 50 to 55 years of life after my heart attack. If you compare the 15 years from the old man and the 55 years from me, my probability of having another heart attack during my 55 years of life is greater than the man who has 15 because of my genetics. Even if I eat absolutely 100% real and non-processed foods, never drink alcohol again, continue not to smoke or use any tobacco products, maintain a stress-free lifestyle, keep physically active and maintain my daily medications, I still have an increased chance of having another heart attack because I have more *TIME* on my clock and my *GENETICS* say so. Dark I know, but it's the truth.

I read a study during my recovery that .6% of men between the ages of 25–39 have a heart attack, then 6.3% between the ages of 40–59, followed by 19.9% between the ages of 60–79 and lastly 32.2% at the age 80+ or older. That is a total of 59% with the other 41% comprised of women following the same age scale. The facts don't lie. I was part of the .6% and came to the conclusion that, even though I lead a healthy lifestyle before, I still had a heart attack because of my genes . . . so it could happen again and I had to be ready.

If someone was able to tell you HOW you were going to die would you want to know? What would you do with that information? Would you give up? Would you start to appreciate the little things and the big things? If you knew HOW, but didn't know WHEN, would that change anything? If Pigtails knew her spelling bee word list beforehand, would she have still studied? Would she have studied for three weeks or the week before, hell, the night before? I believe that was the situation I was facing. I knew, based on my youth and my general time left on this planet, plus my genetic predisposition to cardiovascular disease, I had an increased chance of having another heart attack and dying. I was not 100% sure, maybe 90% sure, but I'm convinced I'll have another heart attack in the next 50–55 years. At that point, life would fulfill its only promise . . . death. See, I said it was dark, but it was a genuine reality I was facing.

Now that I realize HOW I'm going to die, I'm still missing the WHEN, I decide to start living life again. I scavenge what once was my old life and turned it into something new, something better. Not some cliché saying about living life to the fullest, but truly start living life the way I want to, not forgetting the aspects from my previous life that made me happy, successful and proud. I would start living life in the way that sparked our very evolution thousands of years ago. Taking chances, making new friends and putting myself out there to share all while, maintaining a lifestyle of positivity and action, focusing on life instead of death, living among nature and connecting with it was going to be my process. I was going to do exactly what that mysterious on-call nurse said to me 24 hours after beating death . . . help people.

Chapter 5

Scavenge

What does it mean to scavenge? To scavenge in my view is two things: In a metaphorical sense, it's about taking pieces of what has been discarded or has died and mixing it with new ideas, processes and concepts (something old or something new), and adapting or constructing it for *YOUR* use today. The physical aspect of scavenging relates to the definition of resourcing dead animal carcass or plant material for food to survive. I have done both, the metaphorical aspect, and the scavenging predatory kill sites for food when earth-roaming through the mountains. I can tell you they both provide reward in the end and are a key element to survival.

To scavenge in the context of this book is to simply take something from our dead or old past and live off it today and hope it helps us live long into the future. Not all things from our past are dead or bad. We can learn from them, regrow from them or modify them to benefit the current version of 'us'. After having a LAD heart attack known as the widow maker at the age of 37 and almost dying, I spent time reflecting on my life and what I could have done better, different and ultimately what I could do to prevent it. I spent time thinking . . . lots of thinking.

First in a hospital bed, then on short walks around Nana's house and then in caves next to roaring fires. My conclusion was simple, "Stop thinking about what happened and what you could have done different. Use what you know because it works. Just keep on living for today and tomorrow and live better."

I took this new outlook on my heart attack and buried all my pity, anger, humiliation, shame and guilt deep in the mountains, never to unearth it and simply let it rot away until it doesn't exist. I thought to myself that this is the only life I have and I need to dedicate it to my physical self, my mental longevity, my emotional wellbeing and my primal instincts. I can't give my family everything if I'm not mentally, physically, emotionally and primally on track. I began to think about what aspects of life, pre-heart attack, gave me physical, mental and emotional wellbeing. That is when I created scavenging. I scavenged methods and applications from my past to feed my future recovery, as my pre-heart attack pattern of life was not wrong, but needed to be modified or mended in ways. I also scavenged concepts and ideas from other new sources of information and application to aid in my recovery moving forward.

What I have enclosed are those old scavenged and new scavenged applications, methods and attitudes. I still do them all to this day and can tell you they worked for me. Remember, it is *A* way, not *THE* way and this is my way. Maybe when Pigtails spelled her word correctly that day during the fifth-grade spelling bee, nature was telling me and the rest of the world that we can live in many different places, come from different backgrounds, have different points of view, but we are all scavengers in some way shape or form . . . and to never forget that's how we survived.

OLD SCAVENGED

Chapter 6

Engaged Activity

Engaged Activities for me was a key component to my mental and physical recovery after my heart attack. An engaged activity is an activity that eliminates your contemplation and dwelling on a negative event or scenario (like my heart attack), through distraction or complete activity focus. I like to add "the arts" onto my engaged activities as it invokes and fosters the most important survival skill of all . . . creativity.

When asked by students who have enrolled in one of my multi-day hunter/gatherer/ scavenger courses or even a workshop on fire-making methods, students will always ask, "What is the most important survival skill?" I usually reply with a question, "What do you think?" This is only followed by a student barrage of common survival skills like fire making, shelter building, purifying water, food acquisition, navigation, tracking only to end with blank stares and confusion as they quickly have run out of choices. My actions indicate none of them are correct, but I follow up with one statement I live by: "Creativity is the most important," I say, as the stares and confusion deepen. I always follow with a quick perspective that without creativity an earlier version of us and our current model of us would not exist. Creativity and our ability to create has allowed us to survive. We are not born with claws, fangs, scales, fur, and hooves. We don't have the speed of a cheetah, the strength of a gorilla or the flight of a bird, but we have a big brain that fosters and promotes the creative process and that is how we survive. Creativity allowed an earlier version of us to make stone tools to survive and it allowed a cardiac doctor to use a heart stent so that a 37-year-old LAD heart attack patient could survive.

Adding the arts into an engaged activity is important and remember that arts can be anything you want it to be! Arts can be writing, drawing, chainsaw sculpting, rock balancing, weaving, photography, basket making, cooking, flower arrangement, dancing, music, gaming, panning or anything that gives you that sense of distraction and activity focus. I found that when I created something, anything really, and I had that physical outcome in my hands it allowed me to recall the creation of it at a later date and once again provide the distraction I needed. This was a type of physical reflective meditation I created and I will absolutely discuss in a following chapter.

Behind my house I have a small shack with no power that I call the Trapper Shack. The Trapper Shack, or as it's commonly referred to by my wife the Room of Death, is full of animal hides, animal skulls, lithic stone tools, primitive weapons; like Atlatl, stone slings, bows and my personal favorite the primitive throw stick. However, if I hear someone call it a "Man Cave" I tend to get a little defensive as it's far from that. I don't have sports jerseys with some other guy's name written across the back. (Why would I ever do that?) I don't have a built-in bar. I don't have posters of half-naked ladies. I don't have a pool table and most importantly I don't have a sign that says, "Donny's Man Cave." Now, don't get me wrong, if this is your thing and it makes you happy, you do it! I like to live by the saying, "It's *A* way not *THE* way" and there is nothing wrong with your way.

My Trapper Shack is where I created one of my scavenged engaged activities of flintknapping or lithic reduction. Flintknapping in its simplest form is the creation of stone tools through a repeated lithic reduction process using animal bone and antlers as soft percussion devices. Flintknappers typically use obsidians, flint, cherts and any stone that will break in a conchoidal fracture. Stones that break smooth like glass are ideal when compared to a stone like granite that breaks uneven and erratically. The oldest stone tools on record are dated back to over 3 million years ago and predate the earliest humans.

After my heart attack during my recovery I spent hours inside my Trapper Shack creating my own stone tools and designs from cultures past. I would lose track of all time and space and focus on that one piece of stone. It was complete distraction and activity focus. Strike after strike with my new freshly ground moose antler, I was able to slowly unlock a hidden piece of lithic art that remained inside that rock since the creation of our planet. When everything was said and done I could look at the floor of my Trapper Shack and see the stone flakes that had been removed, smell the blood from the tiny flakes cutting my legs, feel the smooth comfort of that treasure from the past in my hands and know that I had in that moment connected with our ancient past as we both — ancient man and modern man — created this same tool to survive. Flintknapping was at that time and is today my engaged activity that helped me in my recovery process. It was my constant distraction from thinking about my heart attack and the probability of having one again in the future. Bottom line, just create something that is you. Make it your own and nobody else's. Use creation as the distraction and focus.

Chapter 7

Earthroamer

Being an *earthroamer* was another one of my scavenged concepts that was important to continue and build upon during my recovery. Now what does it mean to roam? Well, I guess you could pick up any dictionary . . . let's be honest, Nana is the only person I know who uses a dictionary today. Type "roam" into your search engine thing on your computer and you can come up with a number of answers that say: walk aimlessly, move about a large area unsystematically or simply move about. Now add the earth into the equation and you have a person who moves about the earth. That's me . . . an earthroamer.

After dropping out of college at the age of 18 because I already knew everything, I quickly enlisted in the United States Marine Corps. I walked into a Marine Corps recruiting office thinking it would be easy to enlist and it was. I remember the conversation with my recruiter pretty vividly and I bet he still tells the story of, "One day this kid came in . . . ."

Knock . . . Knock . . . Knock

"Hello?" I said, as I gently poked my head through the door that simply read, *The Few, The Proud, The Marines.* I slowly walked through the door and locked eyes with a stern looking man, who was dressed in an immaculate looking uniform that displayed nothing but professionalism and a proud professional warrior.

"I would like to join the Marine Corps" I said in my own weird form of the attention position as I centered myself in front of the professional warrior's desk.

"First off, call me, Sir. Second, when you knock, you wait for the response of, "Come in," before you barge in. Third, what makes you think the Marine Corp, my beloved band of warriors, needs you?"

"Ahhhh . . . well . . . I . . . Sir?" I was a little stunned with the lecture I just received and felt like I had hit bottom. Nevertheless, figured I had nowhere to go but up so just went with it.

"A smooth talker. Shakespeare in the flesh. You must get all the ladies with those sweet lyrics of disappointment," the recruiter said. I could tell he had used those lines before.

"Let me ask you few questions first there, Bon Jovi." *Bon Jovi?* I thought to myself. *Bon Jovi? What the hell*? I thought. *Maybe because I was in Red Bank New Jersey at the time and Bon Jovi lived close by, or maybe I was "Living on a Prayer" thinking I would be able to join* the Marines. An even stranger thought came to my mind, *Maybe I should use Bon Jovi lyrics to pick up the ladies!*

"Eyes on me turd! Are you over 18 years of age, a U.S. citizen, drug free and have no criminal record?" Clearly he was not an interrogator, "Yes, Sir!" Then he sat me down and became human to a degree.

"You like hard work?" pointing directly at my face with all his fingers closed in a way that I would later learn is called the knife hand. It reminded me of a hand chop motion you did when breaking sticks between your buddies hands, but this recruiter used his entire hand instead of a finger.

"Yes, Sir."

"You like being part of something bigger?" with another knife hand pointing directly at my nose.

"Yes, Sir."

"You like a challenge every day?"

"Yes, Sir."

"You like the outdoors?"

"Yes, Sir," I say in an excited, now-we-are-getting somewhere tone.

"You like adventure, seeing the world and doing more in one week than most people will do in their entire life?"

"Yes, . . . yes, Sir," *Keep going,* I think to myself, *Hell yeah!*

"You like the idea of having a lifelong brotherhood that will never die?"

"YES, SIR!" I say in my most excited man-grunt tone of confirmation. The words that followed out of the recruiters mouth were pretty simple and looking back he must've thought *There's a sucker born every day . . . and he just walked into my office.*

The recruiter looked at me with a welcome-to-the-club smirk and said, "Donny you belong in the infantry. You have Grunt 0311 written all over you. Nothing beats the Marine Corps Infantryman. You will become one of Uncle Sam's misguided children, a Leather Neck a real warrior. A life taker and heartbreaker. You know, the ladies love a man in uniform."

Without hesitating and without even thinking I extended my knife hand as he extended his and said, "Sir . . . let's do this. Where do I sign?"

After signing on the dotted line, I attended recruit training at the only place Marines can be born; the beautiful, mosquito infested, sand flea ridden, swamp land called Parris Island, South Carolina. After recruit training, I was directed to report to the School Of Infantry where I learned the fine arts of Marine Corps tactics, techniques and procedures. When everything was said and done, I joined the operating forces and was first stationed in Kaneohe Bay, Hawaii. Not bad for a first duty station.

I found myself in an entire new world. Unfamiliar at first, it soon became my life. A life of brotherhood, honor, courage and commitment. A life of hard work, passion, sacrifice and selflessness. I have seen Marines pull their brothers in arms out of burning vehicles, charge into buildings knowing imminent death could be on the other side and shield a middle eastern woman and her child from enemy fire. Marines . . . no better friend, no worse enemy. In retrospect, becoming a Marine and having travelled to 15 different countries before my 21st birthday was life changing. That same aspect of travel continued well into my adult years in the Marine Corps when I switched jobs into the intelligence field and became an interrogator. My earthroaming started when I was young, but fully developed when I joined the Marine Corps. The Marine Corps fostered the idea to explore and roam about.

Earthroaming in my recovery was vital because I felt free and healthy when I moved about to see new and old places and do it at my determination and control. My first attempt after my heart attack to just walk on my own left me a few houses down from Nana's sitting on a curb struggling to breathe. After I was physically able to walk for at least 15 minutes without stopping, I knew I was on the right road to recovery and could build from that time and progress forward. I built upon that 15 minutes and it soon became 20 minutes, 45 minutes, 60 minutes and then a short run at 20, 30 and 60 minutes. Once I knew I could run for 60 minutes, the earthroamer was back.

My recovery earthroaming was mindless, without direction and all over the Colorado Rockies. I was able to focus on what was beyond the next hill, around the next boulder or down the next valley. Nothing else, just what was ahead of me . . . nothing else but curiosity to lead me. That curiosity focused my attention and attitude on just roaming. No goal, no specific directions, no timeframe . . . just roaming. Having years of survival and primitive living experience aided in my earthroamer abilities allowing for a few hours to turn into a few days of earthroaming. It is possible for any person to earthroam for months with time, effort and education, but other skills are needed. I stayed off the trails, carried very little and slept when I was tired. I drank from springs, consumed wild plants, harvested small game and fish as needed. I slept in caves, was chased by bears, truly living from and with the land. I fully embraced, once again, an earlier version of us and our pattern of life roaming about a virgin world when much about it was still unknown. Following herds, moving from the weather or just roaming the landscape out of curiosity. That curiosity fostered their growth of life and adaptability allowing them to, not just survive, but to thrive.

I still earthroam today and the time spent can be a few hours, to a few days or much longer. My earthroaming today consists of little gear: blade (stone or steel), blanket (wool or elk hide) and a bottle to boil water in. Nature provides everything else. My confidence and abilities in the wilds of the world stem from my days as a child living in Colorado, my time in the Marine Corps and years of survival and primitive living experience. However, I tell more people these days during classes, survival lectures and primitive technology demonstrations to know more and carry less, nature provides, find real sources of information and learn from them. Just go for a walk or an earthroam, start at 15 minutes and build on that. I did that once and wound up exhausted and struggling for air, but I never quit and just kept building from that 15 minutes.

Chapter 8

Eat Wild

Eating Wild was a scavenged concept that was the fuel source to my recovery machine. I had eaten wild before and understood what it meant, however I don't think most people today could fathom the idea in its entirety. Eating wild is just that — eat foods that are wild and only come from the wild. Before you shake your head in agreement that you already do that, let me tell you what it isn't. It isn't organic, all natural, GMO free, free range, cage free, Vegan, Paleo, Gluten free or any other commercialized term to get people to buy food and feel good about it. It is 100% sourced from wild lands by the hand of the one who is eating it.

Eating wild fosters the hunter, gatherer and scavenger in all of us. This historical method is still the current method of eating in some places in the world. Let's manage some expectations for a second. Many people today eat healthy and believe they could eat wild based on the term itself. However, when was the last time you saw a head of broccoli growing along your local hiking trail. When was the last time you were walking your dog and found a bed of carrots? What about cauliflower, pumpkins, lettuce, artichoke, celery and potatoes? Have you seen any of these during your last outing? How about the wild game? When was the last time you consumed rabbit, squirrel, dove, grouse, muskrat, racoon, frog or turtle at your local restaurant? Let's jump up in size for a moment. When was the last time you hunted moose, bear, deer, elk, or bison? Surprisingly enough, large game, small game and fish are consumed within the respected hunting and harvesting seasons pretty routinely, but not as a sole food source. Why is this? How did we forget to eat wild?

Two years ago, I was teaching two Active Duty Army Special Forces Green Berets in some important survival skills they would likely be using in the near future overseas. These guys knew their jobs well. Real professionals, skilled at their craft, but they were looking to brush up a few concepts that required the hand of an expert. We went on a two-day walk into the mountains that started off around 6:00 a.m. The plan that day was to check some traps set the afternoon before, scout for any fresh sign or tracks of animals that we could hunt, and build some primitive weapons. As we were walking to our first set of traps, a familiar aroma filled our noses and caught our attention.

"Smell that?" I asked looking back at them both. We all stopped in such unison that it could have been rehearsed for a Broadway musical.

"Smells like something died," the bigger Green Beret of the two said. Let's just call him Max for this story.

“For sure, smells like death...like fresh blood and meat” We continued to follow our noses over a small hill, until we discovered a nice sized mule deer dead on the ground.

“What the hell?” the other of the two Green Berets said and for this story we will call him Luke.

“I have never seen anything like this before,” Max stated.

Realizing what this was, I say in my most calm and relaxed tone, “This is a fresh mountain lion kill and we are smack dab sitting on top of its breakfast.” I could tell by the steam rising from its body, the bite marks around the neck of the mule deer, prints around the kill and the slight smell of cat urine that this was fresh, maybe 5–10 minutes. “It is very likely that the cat killed its breakfast, started to munch away and then heard us coming and took off. But he isn’t far. He isn’t far and watching us. Alright fellas, let’s move out of here and leave the cat to his prize.”

“No issues here. Let’s roll!” said Luke and motioned to his compatriots to put it in high gear.

“Pussy,” Max whispered softly into Luke’s ear.

I smiled and laughed, remembering how much trash service members and military veterans talk to each other. All three of us began to make our way back to our camp with a bit more trash talking between Max and Luke. All the way back, I couldn't stop thinking that a free meal was on the ground and I should take advantage of it.

"Hold on gents. I'll be right back," I said. "You guys keep going and I'll catch up." Both Max and Luke gave me a thumbs up in acknowledgment. I stealthily, and with complete alertness made my way back to the kill site to cut out a mule deer backstrap for an early lunch. I know that was not the smartest of things, but it had to be done. I was not taking the entire kill, just a piece. The mountain lion earned his meal and I respected that, but I was going to scavenge a piece of food for myself and my tribe (Max and Luke). At the time, in a group, we were the dominant species in the mountains. All three of us together that is, but the playing field was about to level out as I was about to be *ONE*.

When I arrived back at the small hill the smell of death came from a different direction. I slowly walked up the hill just before the crest. I sat for about 90 seconds listening and looking for any sign the big cat was still in the area. I crawled on my belly to the crest just peeking over the hill and saw that the mule deer had been dragged about 15 yards closer to a rocky treeline. I could see the new drag marks as it was covered in blood and showed the cats effort in its tracks to move the kill. Maybe he or she was smaller than I thought. Still no mountain lion to see. I knew he was watching and waiting. I walked slowly down the opposite side of the hill with a slight bend in my knee, eyes alert, ears open with a small four-inch knife in hand ready for whatever might emerge from that rocky treeline. My senses, my awareness and primal instincts were in full force. I felt alive and energized that my meal, my tribe's meal was just a few seconds away . . . and a hidden beast lay watching to see if he was going to have two kills today.

Once at the mule deer, I quickly thrust my knife blade between the shoulders and ran my blade hard and fast along the deer's spine towards its tail. I pulled hard and fast on the meat flap along the mule deer's spine separating the meat from the bone still watching the rocky treeline a few yards away. I implanted my blade a few inches out from my original cut mark and made one parallel cut along the same line of direction towards the tail. I pulled a two-foot piece of meat from the mule deer's back and slowly started to walk backwards to the crest of the hill. I never took my eyes off the rocky treeline as I knew I was under observation. Never in my life have I felt more connected with my primal past. Never in my life have I felt with such certainty that I could be a meal to some other predator. Never in my life have I eaten so wild! I walked back to camp where my two Green Berets students were waiting patiently. At their first sight of me, they spoke almost in unison, "Now I have seen it all!" I explained to them that food comes in many forms and the ability to scavenge food from the wilds may be something, one day they might have to endure. Eating wild is a survival skill that everyone must experience.

During my recovery eating wild was a constant. On a 100% scale I consumed 65%–75% of my meals wild. Again, eating wild means your food source is plants and animals collected from the natural environment by the hand of the consumer. When I'm on an earthroam for a couple of days or more, all my meals are wild, all my liquids are from springs and boiled water from streams and rivers. When it was legal to hunt specific game, I was hunting. When the rains fell and the mushrooms flourished, I collected buckets of mushrooms. When an animal was dead on the side of the road; racoon, deer, possum, rabbit or squirrel and it was still fresh, it was a meal. My wife has a rule in our house that I have to disclose every and anything that she may eat. No surprises. No, "How did you like the possum stew, Eliza?" I collected acorns and pinion nuts when they were in season. I consumed pound after pound of bear berries, rose hips, blueberries, raspberries and many more. I foraged for all sorts of green and their tubers; dandelions, nettles, watercress, sheep's sorrel, burdock, bull thistle, mountain thistle, purslane, mint and wood sorrel to name a few plants found on most forest floors.

Eating wild builds you into a hunter, gatherer and scavenger mindset. It teaches a person not to be picky, but to be appreciative of the wild food opportunities that exist around them. I truly believe that nature provides if you embrace it. I knew eating wild would reset my system, make me feel cleansed, provide a connection to a primal past and promoting my earthroaming. I was able to eliminate sugars, bad carbohydrates and the nasty stuff that is found in our organic commercialized foods. If eating wild sounds like something for you, know that it isn't a modern-day version of a perceived ancient food consumption plan like the Paleo Diet. Purchase a book on edible and medicinal plants. Learn to fish and hunt small game. Find a mushroom expert and learn from them. Establish a relationship with a vetted survival instructor or naturalist and learn from them. Not some character who watched tons of YouTube videos, is 100 lbs. overweight, substitutes gear for knowledge and appropriates the label "survival expert." Watch out for those types. They are bad news . . . and they are everywhere!

Chapter 9

Functional Fitness

Functional fitness was an essential aspect of my heart-attack recovery plan. It was a constant that I applied heavily in my pre-heart attack days and knew it would be a must in moving my recovery forward. Functional Fitness in its simplest definition is training your body to your everyday pattern of life. Instead of working one muscle group you work a group of them or all of them, especially the ones you use every day. Simply put, if you're an office worker and sit at a desk all day for eight hours; what are your body movements and then work those muscle groups.

Here is another take on it. You sit and stand from a chair as you conduct daily activities; you walk two flights of stairs before starting work, at lunch break and when leaving work, you bend over at the waist to load copy paper in a copy machine, and you pull yourself to your desk in your roller chair constantly. Now if we take those body movements and apply an exercise method, it might look like box squats to reinforce your standing and sitting activities, one legged squats to enhance your stair climbs, bent over rows to reinforce your copy machine movements and resistance band pulls to strengthen your roller chair desk slides. All the simple exercise methods reflect your daily pattern of body movements and strengthen them. Most of these body movements can be done at home with simple resistance bands and a chair or even a membership to a gym.

Does it make sense to do a 250 lb. chest press with the above-mentioned daily pattern body movements? Does it make sense to do 150 lb. lat pulldown? No. The aim is to create a program that reflects your daily pattern of body movement and work the muscle groups associated with it. That is why a "muscle head" will put his back out when he leans over to strap in his son in a car seat . . . he has not strengthened or trained the muscles used in that car seat movement.

It doesn't mean you can't jog or go for a hike, but trying to bench press 300 lbs. seems a little counterproductive because you don't play offensive line for the Denver Broncos. As a matter of fact, an athlete like a football player is a great example of when pushing heavy weights away from your body makes sense . . . because that is what an offensive lineman does in his daily work. Take that office worker again and turn them into a firefighter. What are their daily body movements? That is how you build the exercises and strength training; the overall functional fitness plan is based on those daily movements. Think about yourself and your daily motions and start building on them!

In 2006, I was stationed in Okinawa, Japan with my wife and, at that time, our only son. I hadn't made my second son yet, but was trying routinely. I was heading out on a deployment to Iraq about seven months after arriving and was heavy into a functional fitness routine based on what my daily happenings were going to be like when deployed. Near my house in Okinawa, I had access to a stretch of beach that I could train on. I used only what I found on the beach as my fitness tools; driftwood logs, boulders of various sizes and pieces of thick ship rope. I cached some items in the treeline nearby to have a steady supply of fitness tools, but was always curious to see what washed up.

The beach was exactly a .25 miles long and it was my gym. I dragged and carried over my shoulder huge driftwood logs simulating carrying a wounded Marine. I used those same logs and raised them onto a short seawall simulating hauling a body into a medivac helicopter. I sprinted barefoot in the sand. I jumped over large piles of driftwood strengthening jumping into cover. I carried large stones in my hands working out my grip strength simulating ammo cans, fuel cans or water cans. I did hundreds and hundreds of sprints. No matter what I did on that 25 mile stretch of beach, it was tied to my upcoming deployment and the daily pattern of body movements I was going to use to stay alive in Iraq. That is functional fitness at its core!

I hate the gym. I never go. As a matter of fact, the last time I actually outinely went to the gym was before I enlisted in the Marine Corps. I can't stand he smell of body sweat and ass sweat on the machines. The environment is obotic, the attitude of people is stale, the insecurities of the people are depressing and the feeling of being locked up makes me go insane. Where I conduct my exercises to reflect my daily pattern of body movements is in the mountains. I go to the gym outside. Just like my .25 mile stretch of beach in Okinawa, I have locations close to my home that can give me access to the rocks, logs, hills, obstacles and resources I need to conduct my functional fitness ambitions. Keep in mind, my job as a survival instructor keeps me very active so my non-workout days are teaching days, but I'm still active. It's important to add that if I'm not in the mountains teaching or focusing on my functional fitness I still conduct numerous activities; splitting wood for winter, foraging, running, doing tasks around the home, when the snow comes I shovel, I walk my dogs and the list continues.

No matter what, I stay active. Those no teaching days and no functional fitness days have one aim and that is to be active. Some of my best exercises or movements to reflect my daily pattern body movements are; flat timber drags and hill timber drags with various log weights and lengths to strengthen my wood collection muscles used in shelter building, creek jumps of various widths to simulate jumping over creeks while on a hunt or earthroaming; rock/boulder roles used to strengthen my collection of rocks/boulders for shelters, smokers, deadfall traps and fire rings; overhead, between the legs and lateral log/stone throws are used to strengthen my primitive weapon employment like Atlatls, bows, stone slings, rabbit sticks and spears; lots of trail runs on smooth terrain to enhance cardiovascular strength; tree dashes are a 75–100 meter sprint through a wooded area dodging trees, stumps and logs strengthening mobility, balance and body control. I imagine I'm chasing down an animal; rock scrambling up boulder fields strengthening core muscles and enhancing body control to aid in earthroaming; one- or two-legged rock hops simulating silent, game stalking methods enhancing core muscles and balance. I mix in a few others here and there, but these are standard.

On top of this, I always end with one of my favorites! Silent stalks. Silent stalks are where you imagine you must approach an animal or object in the slowest form possible while remaining absolutely quiet — no noise! Your movements are slow. Every foot placement is methodical and purposeful. Breathing is steady, controlled and quiet, not indicating your position. Your eyes stay fixed on one spot; your prey, your target or your threat. Silent stalks can be 20 yards starting out and can lead to the length of an entire valley. Silent stalks are done barefoot with some kind of weapon; knife, bow and two arrows, Atlatl or rabbit stick. (If you don't have one of the mentioned weapons, pick up a log and you have a club.) I like to do silent stalks last when I'm tired, sweaty and sore. I imagine my functional fitness exercises are all the "before" steps our early ancestors took before they finally got to their potential prey and moved in for the kill. If anything, imagine you're about to take a meal from a mountain lion; how silent would you stalk?

There are a few key elements to my functional fitness programs and these should be applied to yours as well:

1. Be standing or crouched when doing any exercise,
2. Always ensure you can focus on the core of the body (that is why we stand),
3. Balance and body control are extremely important,
4. Ensure your flexibility is on track,
5. Range of motion should be good and
6. Use what is around you or what nature provides as your methods to push, pull, squat, lunge, run, jog, ascend, descend, twist, turn and walk.

Now, this is my interpretation of functional fitness and I'm not a certified trainer of fitness. I didn't download a certificate online that I said I'm a functional fitness expert, but I did apply functional fitness in my life before a massive heart attack and used the same fundamentals and methods in my recovery.

Chapter 10

Sleep

Sleep is a must! I hear people all the time say, "I'm so tired," and my thought and typical response is, "Go to sleep. You are not going to miss anything." Why do we not sleep more? Sleep was essential in my heart-attack recovery and it was for sure one of my scavenged recovery methods. I love to sleep at night, nap during the day and doze off when I feel like it. I learned in my cardiac-rehab classes that sleep heals the heart and not enough sleep can cause heart disease, stress, stroke and high blood pressure. So why would we deny ourselves sleep and even more sleep when we need it?

I believe sleep or lack of sleep, commonly called insomnia is a problem. We do so many things during our day to ruin a good night's sleep. When we think about it, our day should have an aspect of focused attention on preparing for a good night sleep. Sounds silly I know, but if you were preparing for a multi-day road trip, would you prepare your vehicle to make that trip? Most people change the oil, check fluids, air pressure, ensure your roadside assistance is good, followed by your license and registration. We take steps to ensure our vehicle operates properly and we need to sleep to ensure our body, the only vehicle we have, can make it day to day!

Today nicotine, caffeine, alcohol, illegal drugs, prescription medications, life stressors, depression, anxiety, sickness, young children, older children, new pets, old pets, ambient noises, roommates, neighbors, lights, work schedules, emotions, bathroom breaks and the screen (TV, phone, tablet, etc.) all cause sleep issues. Knowing this, what steps can you take to mitigate them? Some won't go away until they graduate college, others can be put down, but so many are easy to avoid and control. I'm a realist, however, and I get that some will never change, but you have to take steps to decrease the impact.

My heart-attack recovery sleep was beautiful. I would say during my first two weeks of recovery, 10–12 hours at night and 3–4-hour-long naps. Awesome, I know. As the months continued into recovery and I regained much of my physical and cardiovascular abilities, 7–9 hours a night with a 1–2-hour nap. Still awesome, I know! Today 6–8 hours a night, with a 1–2-hour nap during the day. When I was tired, I slept. Even today, when I'm tired, I take a nap. Why not? What is wrong with going to your car on your lunch break and napping? What is wrong with arriving home and grabbing a quick 1-hour nap before anything else? Nothing is wrong with it. Society has created such a stigma about sleeping or napping during the day that people are seriously creating major physical health problems. The entire world takes naps during the day. Why are we afraid to do it?

The Marine Corps taught me how and where to sleep. When there was an opportunity to get a 45-minute power nap in, you took it because you never knew when the next opportunity to sleep was. You didn't sit around jaw jacking. You closed your eyes and slept! Marines have this amazing ability to sleep anywhere; airport lounges before heading out on a deployment, inside a Port-O-Shitter on a machine gun range — that was me, Private First Class Dust, pants around my ankles, mouth open and out — helicopter rides (guaranteed slumber ops), long as hell resupply convoys during training, in classes, cleaning weapons, conducting preventive maintenance on vehicles — me again, Private First Class Dust, checking for undercarriage leaks, mouth open and snoring — field days, after patrols, lunch breaks, smoke breaks and piss breaks.

Hell, if your ass can grab a few and nobody is going to get killed, have at it. On the flip side, the Marine Corps taught me how not to sleep as well and this is pretty simple; when you're on a mission and when your fellow Marine to your left or right needed sleep more than you. Mission was always priority and troop welfare was always second.

I scavenged that concept of "mission priority and troop welfare second" in regards to sleep during my heart-attack recovery. My mission was to recover from my heart attack and sleep was my key to it. My body needed to heal and recover. I did not want to rush it. However, I eliminated much of the insomnia contributors thereby enhancing my personal welfare (troop welfare); no alcohol (still none today), no nicotine, no caffeine after a certain time, no food after 8:00 p.m., no TV in bedroom — my wife and I will never get one as we would rather be doing other things — no technology, go to bed void of emotion, eliminate hot temperatures, eliminate light, install soothing ambient noise and if one is having trouble sleeping we don't rustle around or wake the other. This is my general model for sleeping at home today and it still produces 6–8 hours of sleep at night.

When I'm in the backcountry teaching, hunting, gathering, scavenging or earthroaming my sleep is amazing. My naps during the day are even better. I love sleeping in caves, improvised shelters, large piles of leaves and grass, in animal hides, in the open, on sunny hillsides full of flowers and berries, in a rainstorm protected from above, in falling snow and, the most important of all, next to a fire, man's first TV! Sleeping wild is awesome as many of the "insomnia" factors don't exist at all. You see, your priorities change, and mental focus is trained on ensuring your safety and warmth during the night, not what someone you will never meet and holds no personal value to you said about you online. Let's be honest, credit card debt worries don't survive in the wilds, especially when you're sleeping under the stars, next to a fire in a bed of leaves and grass.

Bottomline, you have to sleep to recover, recharge and reconnect to yourself and the world around you. When you're tired, sleep. When you need to recharge, sleep. If you know what keeps you from getting those precious hours, eliminate it. Get rid of the screens and televisions in the room. Sleep in darkness, and with soothing sounds or no sound. Quit the nicotine, caffeine and alcohol; or at least reduce the amounts. Think that your body is a machine and one of the best fuels for this amazing, one-of-a-kind machine is sleep.

Chapter 11

Time

Time and really the management of it was a scavenged concept from my past that flowed perfectly into my heart-attack recovery program. Time for you and your health are essential. Time for engaged activities and sleep are a must. Time for family and friends; and sometimes nothing at all are important. I hear from people all the time that, "There are not enough hours in the day to get things done." I have to disagree with this. There are plenty of hours in the day, but *YOU* can't manage those hours and prioritize them properly.

After my heart attack, time was mine and I made sure I used time for what I wanted and needed. The best way I was able to manage my individual time and family time was communication. I let my family know what I needed to accomplish and the steps involved. I never told, but educated them on the importance of my earthroaming, functional fitness and engaged activities to my heart-attack recovery. I was able to accomplish many things as I was excellent at creating time and allocating time to tasks or objectives properly.

The best ways to create time is to stop giving a shit about the irrelevant stuff in your life. Some actions I took to create more time are as follows:

1. Say, "No," or even better say, "Hell no!" You don't have to agree to everything. If a friend becomes irate because you said, "No" to meeting up for drinks after work, well that is not a friend and they don't value your time. Say, "No" if it doesn't benefit you. Stop doing things you don't like doing. Trust your instincts.

2. Limit social media posts and responses. To be honest, I only started with social media three months after my heart attack as it has never been a huge factor in my life, but, for some of you, just limit yourself. Mine social media promotes my business and enables me to communicate with others. Don't do it when you're driving, don't do it during your lunch break (eat your mushrooms and venison) and don't do it when you could be spending time with loved ones. I get it, social media is a thing and it's a way to stay informed of family, news, local events, but keep it to 30 minutes. Nobody really thinks the photo of your sushi is life changing.

3. Stop answering your phone. I hardly answer mine. If you're calling me to shoot the shit and see what's up, leave a message and I'll call you back. If I'm busy doing something, well I'm busy. When did we lose our sense of ownership and the balls to not answer our phones? I used to love it when people would eventually get hold of me a day or two later and say, "I called you! Why didn't you pick up?" and my easiest and best response that destroyed all morale was, "Because it's my phone and I was busy." That is usually followed by, "Busy doing what?" To which

my usual response is, "Whatever I wanted." That pissed so many people off, but it *is* my phone and if it was life or death they would call again and leave a message.

4. Do important things first! I simply mean important things that are factors in your life not the superficial stuff that provides no value. Things that promote your wellbeing, the family's wellbeing, mindfulness, sleep, health and business if you have one. Don't forget sex. Sex is important! Have a quickie or get nasty (or romantic) with your significant other. That is always a priority. If it's work time, do things that make you money or promote your business. Read to your kids, go to their events, promote them and their success as that is time well spent. Take time for you to do you; earthroam, eat wild, engage in functional fitness, sleep, have sex and have more sex. Do the important things first!

5. Get organized. Stop procrastinating and get your shit together. Nobody thinks it's cool to be almost 40 and disorganized. You can be free spirited, autonomous, spontaneous and still be organized. That's called being a leader. When your life is cluttered and scattered about, that is time wasted. Have simple daily schedules to facilitate processes and accomplish tasks. Write them down in a small book or notepad, keep it off your phone and stick to it. Write it down and keep writing it down! Organization is the key to executing processes to accomplish tasks and have the freedom and the time to do what you want later.

6. Make a decision. Too much time is wasted thinking about all the options. Sure, weigh out the pros and cons, but it should not be an hour-long process to pick a restaurant, the best day hike or what you should wear. When it comes to investments or big life-changing ideas, a different approach may be required, but we are talking about simple decision making for day-to-day living. Make a decision and go with it. Just pick one and go. One of the hardest things to do for some people is to make a decision. It's OK to be wrong, learn from it and move on.

7. Teamwork makes dreamwork. That's right, teamwork. Delegate tasks and authority, utilize a cooperative effort and divide and conquer. I have two sons with two different schedules after school. Usually it can be executed by one person, but sometimes I use Nana as she is always ready to get her hands dirty. People need help at times. It is OK to ask for it. If you have a team, tribe or posse use them. You don't have to do everything yourself. If you're a solo act, figure it out and get it done.

I applied all of these time management actions all the time during my heart-attack recovery. I needed time to recovery and I was going to ensure I had it. Like I said before, I created time and used it for what I wanted and needed. Time is just that a numerical value placed on a day. Our ancestors prioritized their actions and efforts for their personal betterment and the tribe's overall wellbeing. Imagine if you could do the same. Focus your efforts that promote your wellbeing and your tribe's wellbeing and cut out all the other bullshit. You would be surprised how much extra time you have to truly do the things you love.

Chapter 12

Never Set Goals

Never set goals! I can't say it enough. I can't stand it when people use words like, "long-term goals" or "short-term goals" or "goal action plan" and the best one of all "goals need to be specific, measurable, attainable, realistic and timely." What a bunch of crap. In my heart-attack recovery plan, I never set goals. I focused on the process. My approach was just do it and get it done. I find goals to be a person's way to limit their real potential to explore and create. Many times people who are not you set your goals for you. I bet people love it when their boss or manager calls them in for a "professional development" meeting and tells them what their goals are going to be. Talk about crushing someone's motivation? Telling them their ideas don't matter is a sure way to not reach any goals at all.

Goals can create anxiety and stress if you're not progressing to the goal nilestone. For some people, this can lead to serious depression if you fail. Goals ılso cause people to over-focus on one thing and neglect the others. If your goal is o lose 25 lbs. and be healthier and you're still puffing on a pack of cigarettes a ay, you could lose even 50 pounds and still be blind to the cigarettes. Goals cause eople to take extremes to achieve that goal. Oftentimes people will conduct unethical or irrational behavior to achieve the goal. More importantly, goals often stifle and extinguish creativity. We all know creativity is the number one survival skill. I think a wise man once said that . . . . Or was it me?

I worked for a government contracting company as soon as I left the Marine Corps in 2011 and it was a nightmare. I hated every minute of it. This company was a corrupt system full of fraud, waste and abuse. I had one "manager" that sat me down for a goal setting session and I can recall the conversation to this day.

"Donny, we need to establish your goals for the upcoming period," and before I could get a word in, "I have a couple in mind that I think would work well for you."

"Please go on," I said, "let me know what you think I should have for goals." Without taking a breath the manager listed out eight or nine goals that were completely foreign to my thinking. The goals he listed made no sense to my pattern of life or scope of work. I could tell he was nervous and from his rehearsed speech I knew he had practiced this theatrical monologue a few times alone in his office.

I should add that I did not fit in to the company culture. I had a long beard, a body full of tattoos, did not kiss ass and did not pull any punches. I said it how it was, with tact and intensity. I guess spending over a decade in the Marine Corps will do that to you.

After the theatrical monologue was complete, I looked him square in the eyes knowing that much eye contact would make him uncomfortable and simply said, “Nope, those don’t work”

“What do mean, ‘those don’t work’?”

“Goals are shit and those goals are shit. If you want me to do something and it’s aligned to this task, no issues. I’ll get it done, but I don’t do goals . . . goals are for people who don’t achieve success every day,” I said, never taking my eyes off him.

I could tell he was shocked by my statement, because he said nothing. He got up and walked out and the goal conversation was over. I received a written letter of reprimand for my “Harsh tone and unwillingness to participate in professional development.” I chuckled slightly when I received it because apparently “words hurt” and so do “harsh tones.” Goal setting focuses on the result and not the process. The process is the key to the result. Goals create a hyper focused state of mind that completely overlooks the process. If you’re trying to lose pounds, the process is the exercise and implementation of a proper diet, not dropping the 15 pounds. If you’re trying to recover from a heart attack, engaged activity, earthroaming, eating wild, functional fitness, sleep and time management are the process.

I get it. Not everyone has the autonomy to just be themselves, create as they see fit and establish their processes, but for all that is natural don't fall prey to the bogus goal construct. I don't set goals, but focus on processes to accomplish what needs to be accomplished. All you will be doing is reinforcing a flawed reward system. You do you and focus on the process.

NEW SCAVENGED

Chapter 13

Fasting

Fasting — who knew? Down my road to recovery after my heart attack, I scavenged the idea of fasting from some research on ancient primitive cultures and their ceremonial practices. I'm always reading about our ancient past and started to see trends in fasting. I found that ancient primitive cultures fasted for a variety of reasons to include a physical reset of the body, spiritual reset, pre-wartime actions, rites of passage ceremonies and religious ceremonies. Today people fast in protest, and for health and lifestyle reasons. The health benefits today are endless when it comes to fasting and I can tell you it was life changing for me in my heart-attack ecovery.

My fasting practices are simple. I consulted with my cardiologist before partaking in any serious fasting activities and I recommend everyone do the same. n all actuality, I consulted with several nurses and doctors I know. Not one of hem had anything negative to say about fasting. Additionally, my fasting occurred n two places: at home, and in the mountains earthroaming.

1. 24-Hour Fast: My 24-hour fast is pretty simple. In one 24-hour period, there is no eating except between the hours of 4:00–8:00 p.m. During those four hours the meal and snack consumed are wild or all natural. Eat one snack of fruit, berries, nuts or raw greens around 4:15. Keep it to a single serving size and avoid overeating. Have your meal around 7:00 ensuring you eat some of the following: fresh greens, veggies, egg, soup or broth, dried fruits, fish, game birds, wild meat or all-natural meat. Avoid breads, pastas or grains or anything that comes in a box. I also avoid milk and dairy products. Never been a huge fan of them, so they don't belong in my pattern of life. Eat vibrant colorful food. During the full 24-hour day, drink water, lots of it. Water is an awesome way to hydrate and cleanse your body. Drink black coffees and teas throughout the day. Avoid the caffeine if possible and the crazy amount of sugar people drink with coffee. A wild pine needle tea, rose hip tea, or Labrador tea are great before you head off to bed. Remember to stay hydrated!
2. 40-Hour Fast — My 40-hour fast is done twice a month. In one 40-hour period, there is no eating only drinking of fluids. A good example of my 40-hour fast is as follows: Thursday I consume my last meal no later than 8:00 p.m. (tying into the end of the 24 hour fast) and drink a tea (caffeine free) before heading to bed.

Friday is a full day of no food. Feel free to drink black coffee, teas, water and water infused with all-natural fruit, but don't eat the fruit! Be active that day! Earthroam, get involved with your engaged activities and perform some functional fitness.

Saturday I wake up, hydrate, drink coffee, have a cup of tea and between 12:00–2:00 p.m. I eat my first meal as the 40-hour fast has concluded. This first meal must be small and not overbearing. Your stomach has shrunk and too much food is only going to come back up or make you feel terrible. I stick to a bone broth, beef broth or veggie broth. Have a single serving of nuts and a small snack of berries, fruit or a hardboiled egg. Spread the consumption out over the two-hour block between 12:00–2:00 p.m. Do not gorge yourself. My next meal consumed is between 4:00–8:00 p.m. and resembles the 4:00–8:00 p.m. meal you consume during the standard 24-hour fast. Do not gorge yourself. Eat slow and if you're still full from your first consumption, don't rush it. This is why I worked in a window rather than a hard-set time.

3. 7–10-Day Fast. My 7–10 day fast is conducted three times a year. I mark it on a calendar and aim for those dates, but keep it flexible. The 7–10-day fast resembles the 40-hour fast, but for 7–10 days. The key thing to remember during the 7–10-day fast is staying hydrated. I actually take in calories during the 7–10-day fast. This is done through a bone broth (my favorite), beef broth or veggie

broth (homemade veggie and beef broth work the best). Additionally, I drink honey water (8 oz water, 1 tsp of honey) and fresh lemonade or water infused with fruit (don't eat the fruit). Yes, I'm taking in calories, but they are minimal.

4. During the 7–10-day fast, I consume my first broth at the 40-hour mark (exactly like the 40-hour fast). I continue with broths between 4:00–8:00 p.m. every day until the fast is over. I never take in more 16 oz of broth during that 4:00–8:00 p.m. window. I also drink a glass of honey water at 12:00 every day starting on the third day (also when I have my first broth). Black coffee, tea, lemonade (real lemons people) and fruit infused water is consumed whenever I want.

Coming off the 7–10-day fast, or breaking your fast, needs to be done carefully. Too much food, too soon can lead to stomach issues, G.I. Tract complications, vomiting and an all-around feeling of crap. Take it slow. That's why it's 7-10 days. On the day I break my fast (Day+1), at the broth consumption between 4:00-8:00 p.m. I add in some veggies (carrots, celery, onion, etc.) into the broth. Don't overdo it. Please trust me!

The next day (Day+2), I have a breakfast consisting of one or two hard boiled eggs and one cup of fruit either melon, banana or apple. That meal I shoot to eat between the hours of 9:00–10:00 a.m. I'm still drinking water, coffee, lemonade and fruit infused waters. I drink a honey water at 12:00 noon followed with my broth consumption between 4:00–8:00 p.m. In this broth, I include veggies, but also add in small amounts of meat, poultry, or fish and have a desert of berries or fruit if I feel OK.

The next day (Day+3), I shoot to eat between the hours of 9:00–10:00 a.m. and consume hard boiled eggs, fruit and sometimes a small amount of meat or fish (I avoid sausages and bacon). I drink a honey water at 12:00 noon just like the day before. Between 4:00–8:00 p.m. I have small cup of broth with veggies and add in meat, poultry or fish. I have a standard meal consisting of a small sweet potato (or regular potato), fish (or other serving of meat), boiled greens and another vegetable. The next day (Day+4), I do it all over again providing a little more food each meal. Again this takes time and effort, but the rewards are amazing.

Why should you fast? Well, that is for you to discover. Everyone is different and as always, this is *A* way, not *THE* way of doing something. What I provided above was my way. Scavenge it if you like! Fasting was essential in my heart-attack recovery. I enjoyed the cleansing effect it had on my body. My mind was clear, my internal system felt clean and I enjoyed the process. For someone who eaches survival, primitive skills and wilderness self-reliance; it's awesome to onvey, convincingly that a person can go for periods of time with minimal food nd still make it out alive. Fasting for me was a controlled method to realign my body and mind, manage weight, promote healthy living and experience a component of life from our past.

Chapter 14

Grounding

Grounding is awesome! It is a scavenged idea and method, but something I have always done without realizing it. Grounding (sometimes called Earthing) is our physical electrical connection to the earth. The earth is like a giant battery and has some natural electrical elements that our body can benefit from. I'm not a scientist and can't give you all the technical concepts behind grounding, but I can only tell you what it did for me in my heart-attack recovery and what it does for me today.

I'm not one to wear shoes if I don't have to. When I do, it's moccasins, leather sandals or a hiking type shoe. Social protocol dictates that I must wear them at certain times; fifth grade spelling bees, airports, jury duty and local establishments, but when I'm in the mountains, woods, jungles or any part of this wild world, no shoes. I have been doing this for some time now and can tell you that when I'm "free-toeing," I feel awesome, energized and focused. I run barefoot, earthroam barefoot, hunt barefoot and pretty much do everything barefoot. Grounding for me in my heart-attack recovery gave me physical balance, deeper sleep, more energy and a spiritual connection to our ancient past.

Grounding in all actuality is a catchy and hip name for something we have always done. We are not born with shoes on so why do we do it? Our ancestors in more harsher climates needed foot protection from extreme exposure and developed footwear, but still walked barefoot. From a protection standpoint footwear is and can be beneficial, but can also limit mobility and the wearer's connection to the earth.

After spending a couple days earthroaming in some remote areas of Colorado, I jumped on a trail to finish the last half-mile trek to my car when I came across two hikers — a man and a woman in their late 20's — decked out in the finest outdoor clothing apparel money could buy: huge hiking boots, trekking poles, hats, compass, sleeping pads, water bottles, sunglasses and who knows what else on the inside of their packs. Their packs were monstrous; at least 50–55 lbs. at best guess. The only thing that separated the two from being identically dressed was that the lady had a Colorado Native hat on. If you're from Colorado and were born there, people believe they earned the right to wear and display a "Native" sticker on just about everything and anything. Her poor fiancé, he must have felt like a hostage to her and all that gear! Our conversation went something like this:

"Hey, how's it going?" I said, as I walked by.

"Great and yourself?" they asked almost in unison.

"Fine, thanks for asking. Enjoy your time. The mushrooms are really starting to pop!" I said as I quickly walked by. Now let me describe how I was dressed; no shoes, cut off pants that are now shorts, a multi colored Baja jacket ($15.00 at my local gas station), a waist wrap containing a metal water bottle, a few morsels of dried meat, hand-drill, friction-fire set and a stone knife hanging in a leather pouch around my neck.

"Excuse me, sir," the Hostage said, "I don't mean to bother you, but do know if this trail connects with the Colorado trail?" the Hostage continued with "My fiancé and I are doing two nights out here and we were hoping it connected to the Colorado Trail."

"Sorry dude, I don't know. I just jumped on this trail knowing it leads to my .ruck. Sorry."

"It's all good," the Hostage said. "Just thought I would ask."

"Sorry. I wish I could have helped you," I said, one last time.

"Where are you coming from?" the Native asked.

I pointed to a distant mountain peak and said, "I camped out last night on the .vestern side of that peak." I continued with, "It has a small lake full of trout, more f a pond really, but tons of trout."

The Native asked, “Just one night? We are doing two.” I thought the Native and her Hostage could probably do a month with the amount of gear they had on their backs and strapped to their packs.

“That’s awesome,” I said. “This is day six for me, so last night was night five . . . .” After a few minutes of conversation with a bit of bitchiness from the Native, I explained that there was no trail to my trout pond, but if they aimed for the mountain, they couldn’t miss it. After a few more minutes of discussing my lack of “gear” and my ability to live from the land, the guy pointed to my feet and said, “You must be into Grounding.”

I had no idea what the Hostage was talking about. “Grounding?” I said, “What is that?”

“You know . . . Grounding. Walking barefoot and drawing your energy from the earth. That type of thing.”

“Never heard of it,” I said. I really thought to myself, *What the hell is this guy talking about?*

“Oh, man, you have to check it out,” the hostage continued. “I don’t do it all the time, but I think it’s something I’m going to do more of”

“That’s dumb. Why would you walk around with no shoes. It’s just silly,” the Native said.

I looked at the Native and her Hostage and said, “Sounds like a thing. I will for sure look into it,” I said. “Thanks for the information.” I wished the Hostage good luck on his two days in the backcountry.

At that point, I told the Natives and the Hostage that I would look into Grounding and appreciated the conversation, but I had to get going. When I got home, I was shocked to find that “Grounding” was a thing. I never really had a term for physically and electrically connecting with the earth, but it worked in my recovery. I don’t know how it exactly worked, but I felt better, slept better, felt stronger, had very little stress and was centered. It could be that most of my grounding takes place in the woods and that is my environment, but even at home, I had the same results. Give it a shot! All you have to do is pop those shoes off, walk barefoot across the earth and see what happens.

Chapter 15

Find My Tribe

Finding my tribe is really making new friends. Apparently, it's a thing. We are a social species and need human contact in many forms. That is how we survived as a species and that is how we survive today. We need relationships and we need *NEW* relationships as we grow into life. There is nothing wrong with holding on to friends from the past, but as we change, our relationship and friend criteria change as well. However, that was not always my point of view.

I'm a solo dude by nature. I have two older sisters with me as the youngest by several years. I moved around a lot and found that my tribe over the long term only consisted of myself. I had no problem making friends. As a matter of fact, I always had them, good friends to be precise, but never really saw the value of keeping them once our lives went in different directions. Along with being independent, solo and a tribe of one, nature was a constant friend. In the Marine Corps I had tons of brothers-in-arms, compatriots, and bros, but having left the Marine Corps in 2011, I still don't have any regular happenings with any of them. like pursuing my interests on my own, at my discretion and with complete autonomy. However, after my heart attack all I wanted to do was reconnect with people from the past, build new relationships and find my tribe.

I scavenged the idea of making new friends from my wife. She has tons of them. She still keeps in frequent contact with her friends from elementary, high school and college. I'm amazed by this and how she does it. She could go without talking to a college friend for a year and pick up where they left off as if that year never existed. For me, not so much. I just never have maintained a serious level of commitment to people aside from my wife. She recommended I find new friends that have similar interests to mine and share what I know. How I was going to do this was through social media. *Kill me now*! was my first thought. I did not want social media in any way, shape or form. I despised it and believed it to be of no value.

I was wrong. I joined several of the standard social media platforms Facebook, Instagram, YouTube, and Pinterest) underneath my business name to keep focused on why I was doing it: reconnect with past relationships, establish new relationships and promote my business through sharing what I know. I quickly found out that there were people out there like me, that had very similar interests. Some were local and some were in different geographic locations. It was fun to have conversations with people that were similar to me and did not judge me for my interests.

On Facebook, I was able to reconnect with people from my past that were important to me then and are important to me now. Plus, I was able to send birthday cards on time because Facebook keeps track of birthdays! Who knew? On Instagram, I could share my stories, adventures and my artistic side. I could also share in other people's adventures and found it rewarding.

My wife also brought up the point that I had much to give. I had years' and years' worth of information and experience that I should share with people on YouTube. All that I know and do almost went down with the ship — knowledge not shared is knowledge lost. I created a YouTube channel and started sharing skills that I have through that platform. I started writing articles for popular survival, homesteading and woodsmen magazines. I truly enjoyed the creative process.

I joined some different groups and left many of those groups. I met new people that I'm happy to call friends today and don't communicate with others because some people are just too damn negative. Bottomline? I started to open up and put myself out there. I wanted to be able to share my success and failures with others, have a sense of belonging and meet people with similar interests. I stopped caring what people thought. To be honest, I never cared what people thought abou me. I have always had the mental and physical ability to stand up for myself. The best response to negativity is silence. I believe opening up, connecting with old relationships, and making new friends was very healthy for me and aided greatly in my heart-attack recovery. I still remember to keep my actions and efforts on social media to a bare minimum, but I see a value in it today. People need people. We have to remember that is how we survived and that feeling of community was the cornerstone of any tribe.

Chapter 16

Physical Reflective Meditation

Physical reflective meditation is a scavenged concept from what is called reflective meditation. I added the "physical" part as the practice was something I was doing without knowing what it was in my heart-attack recovery. Reflective meditation is a form of meditation that is focused or controlled thinking. A person determines a reflection point like a theme, subject, question, problem, or topic to reflect on. All aspects of thought are focused on the reflection point in a controlled manner. During the reflection time, the topic, subject, theme problem or question is analyzed, solved, evaluated or scrutinized; drawing out outcomes and solutions.

My method of physical reflective meditation is similar in ways to reflective meditation, but different in others. Let me break it down. Many people hold onto physical pieces of the past, things like heirlooms, awards, medals, trophies, pieces of art, trinkets, knick knacks, baby shoes, locks of hair, etc. Literally anything can be a piece of the past as long as it holds an emotional value to the person holding onto it. For example, your grandfather passed away and he left you his old knife that was his as a kid, maybe your mother quilted a blanket for you before you left for college and you still have it, or the collar of a beloved family pet that passed not long ago all present a physical reflective object. This physical reflective object provides the focal point to reflect on. No other thoughts or objects are allowed in your mind as you touch, feel, see and smell the physical reflective object.

Why I adapted reflective meditation to become my own scavenged, physical reflective meditation is pretty simple. Physical reflective objects from our past can help us reflect on the future through the physical properties of the object itself. Physical reflective meditation empowers and heightens more of our senses with a deeper focus on the physical reflective object and how it relates to our reflection subject. For example, you're 37 years old and have a massive heart attack and almost die leaving all that you know and love forever. The days following, you have feelings of doubt, sadness and unanswered questions as to how this could have happened. You question your own future and the probability of your death. You start to reflect on times past and what they meant to you. You discover in a drawer a small baby food jar full of sea glass. You open the jar and pull out one piece of dull blue sea glass and hold it in your hands. You close your eyes and instantly recall wandering along sun bleached beaches searching for sea glass with your wife and sons. Searching for the perfect pieces. You can feel the ocean air on your skin, you can see the breeze gently moving your wife's hair. With every rotation of the sea glass in your hands a new memory takes claim to your mind. You remember that on this day, the day of the sea glass, the day of ocean breezes gently touching your face and sand in between your toes, was the day before you left for war.

Your eyes open with the sea glass still in hand and you realize that this near-death experience — the heart attack — doesn't compare to those of the past. You come to the conclusion that death is imminent and can happen at a moment's notice. It can come from a bullet, it can come from a bomb, maybe a car, a hungry mountain lion, a bear or even a heart attack, but no matter *HOW* death comes we will never know *WHEN* death comes. So, live your life to the fullest and live each day as if it's your last.

Physical reflective mediation was a very powerful form of mediation for me. It made my recovery better and kept my outlook very positive. I can take objects from my past and reflect on them for the future. I can find objects to be used in the future as well and focus on positive outcomes that *WILL* come from them. Objects hold a value and connection to the past. Open your mind and heart to them and anything can happen

When I meditate, I find a quiet place and get to down to business. My most enlightening and deepest forms of physical reflective meditation come when I'm alone, outside during sunset or sunrise. Additionally, sitting next to a fire physical reflecting on the past to impact the future is something everyone needs to experience. Pick any object, focus on it, remember how it was made, when it was given to you, how you found it and what it means to you. Does it have a story? Does it connect you with times past? Does it connect you to the future? Does it speak to you? Are you listening? I believe, and this is based on my experience and outcomes that much peace can be obtained through some form of meditation. I found my scavenged form of physical reflective meditation to be the most beneficial to me. Come up with *A* way, not *THE* way that works best for you.

Chapter 17

Forest Bathing

Forest bathing is a scavenged concept that I always did, but never really had a name for. Through the use of social media, someone shared a post describing the concept and what is also known as, *Shinrin-Yoku* or “taking in the forest atmosphere”. *Shinrin-Yoku* is traditionally a form of healing and preventive health care for many people in Japan, where people spend time in the forest. Maybe having lived in Okinawa, Japan for some time and being a lover of the outdoors, *Shinrin-Yoku* evolved into a form of healing and health care for me. I employed this concept unintentionally at first as I was always outside, but after learning of it, I scavenged the idea and made it my own.

The basic concepts of forest bathing are pretty simple. Find and visit a forest or natural area. Move among it slowly, breathing in the air, listening to the sounds, feeling the elements and just relaxing. Or another way to forest bathe (and my preferred way) is to simply find a spot in the forest, sit, stand or lay on the ground, have some aspect of your skin touch the natural environment and ground yourself to the earth. Breathe slowly, eliminate movement, listen to the sounds around you, feel the natural occurrences (air, rain, sun, wind, etc.) and relax. There are no time limits, there is no specialized gear or set of movements to degrade your connection to the forest. Just be . . . .

Forest bathing has many health benefits. People from all over are applying forest bathing in their everyday health and fitness regiments. Some benefits that I discovered through my frequent forest bathing sessions during my heart-attack recovery are:

1. A sense of happiness,
2. Fulfillment,
3. Increased energy,
4. Improved mood,
5. Reduction of stress, and
6. An overall feeling of connection to the land.

Before my heart attack, I conducted forest bathing routinely, but with a wist. My twist was adding the occurring elements to my forest bath if you will. If t was raining, I forest bathed in the rain, or even the snow. Whatever the weather nd environmental factors were that day, I embraced it and knew it was the natural tate to be in.

Routinely, I found myself lying on the ground on my back, half naked, eyes losed, just taking it all in — the sights, smells and the touch of everything around e. Sometimes, I would sit high above on a cliff, inside a cave, covered in mud, sunburned, dehydrated and sometimes sitting in an ice-cold stream. Yes, my method was different than traditional forest bathing, but it was my way and I felt better every time I did a version of it.

Forest bathing in the more traditional sense or my scavenged version of it, is the first step for some people to invoke their primal past and rejoin the natural world. For me, forest bathing has always been a *thing*. It never really had a name, but it always felt right. I recommend it to people all the time. I tell them to go out in the natural world and just be. Be *there* for yourself and nobody else. Spend some time connecting to world around you and you may discover a side of you that has been long lost. Embrace that new, long-lost discovery and your world could entirely change.

Chapter 18

Pilgrimage

Pilgrimages for me are a must. Like the common definition says, a pilgrimage is: "When a person makes a long journey to visit a place of religious significance, considered special or of personal importance." Partaking in a pilgrimage was a scavenged concept from my past that was a huge aspect of my heart-attack recovery. I'm not a very religious person, but knew taking a pilgrimage or two during my recovery, out of the state of Colorado to a place that was of personal importance was going to be a key aspect of my recovery. A pilgrimage, outside of your local area is important. The pilgrimage, encompassing the travel and destination, can provide a great deal to a person, especially to someone who is in recovery from a health issue or trauma.

Taking a pilgrimage promotes a person's communication/social skills as the travel requires us to communicate with everyone — cab drivers, hotel workers, travel companions, local vendors, retailers, local authorities and guides, typically in different dialects or languages. Pilgrimages enable people to cope with uncertainty and reinforce their tolerance for, as many people know, travel plans are never 100% and can often change easily. A pilgrimage promotes creativity as a person can experience new food, people, weather, clothes, problems, ideologies, cultures and destinations fostering new ideas and originality. A pilgrimage also builds confidence, giving people a sense of accomplishment and adventure. Most importantly, people partake in a pilgrimage because of the spiritual or personal significance of the location. Accomplishment of the pilgrimage can segue into mindfulness, peace and give a sense of fulfillment. Conducting a pilgrimage can bring awareness, illuminate thoughts and ideas, while directing focus to the important things in life.

Pilgrimages have been part of our ancient past. Ancient cultures made pilgrimages to offer sacrifices to their gods, promote religious and cultural ideas, to heal from sickness or to ask for forgiveness. Even today, many cultures make pilgrimages for a variety of reasons. Some people today take pilgrimages focused more on the spiritual or religious side, while others might be taking a pilgrimage to attend a sporting event at their favorite athletic team's stadium several states away. For me, taking a pilgrimage is about the personal connection to the destination and the travel to get there.

I have taken so many pilgrimages that it's hard to account for them all, but some elements for me that make a great pilgrimage are:

1. a location that holds an emotional significance,

2. a location that has a cultural impact that is outside of your normal pattern of life,
3. a travel plan that is historical in the route and the destination,
4. a pilgrimage that is nothing but leisure based,
5. a pilgrimage that connects with a personal spiritual belief whatever it may be, and
6. who you take a pilgrimage with; wife, family, kids, best friends or just yourself.

Nothing wrong with going about it solo, but having a tribe with you makes it that much better. No matter what, you do you!

Closing

So, if you haven't figured out yet why having a massive heart attack at the age of 37 was the best thing could have happened to me and the people around me, here you go: First, my heart attack was the perfect example to people that, "It can happen to anyone. It can happen to you!" Like I told Rick while lying in a hospital bed, "I don't mind being the example and hopefully people can learn from me." This made me feel better. This made me a better person and by me becoming better person, I was able to mentally, physically, emotionally and primarily influence the people in my life to become better than they were yesterday. If it could happen to me it can happen to you . . . trust me! If you're reading this book maybe you can walk away with one or two things to make your mind, body, emotions and primal instincts feel better.

Second, I also figured out HOW I'm going to die. I feel pretty fortunate to have a leg up on death and I don't fear it. I'm still trying to figure out the WHEN, but in all honesty, I don't care because I make each day count. I hold nothing back. I spend time teaching survival skills, primitive skills and wilderness self-reliance because I love it. I partake in awesome adventures and challenges whenever I can with no regrets. I make love to my wife all the time. I still attend spelling bees, sporting events, and I still get First Five in carpool pickup and I earthroam barely clothed through the wilds of the world just being me.

Third, in the wake of my heart attack, amazing things happened. I was able to really self-reflect on all parts of my life. I watered old dying relationships that were still important to me. I established new relationships more centered on my pattern of life and interests. I also started to share more of who I'm with the world. I have much to give and the giving continues today. I also found meaningful ways to positively reflect on the past for the betterment of my future.

Finally, you now know setting goals is not my thing and never will be. The process is more important. Well, congratulations you now know my process to prevent and prolong the WHEN and even the HOW! Isn't that what life is all about, not dying, not fearing death, but acknowledging that it happens while still living a long, happy and healthy life. Hopefully you can walk away with something scavenged from this book that will impact your own future.

Remember, all the things described in this book — engaged activity, earthroaming, eating wild, functional fitness, sleeping, time management, never setting goals, fasting, grounding, finding your tribe, physical reflective meditation, forest bathing and pilgrimages are all tools that empower me to live a certain lifestyle and that lifestyle enabled my recovery from a massive heart attack at the age of 37. The only life you have is what you have right now. Don't waste it. Don't let death, almost dying or even the idea of death impact your life. Live your life and love your life. Welcome to my tribe!

“Death is a challenge. It tells us not to waste time . . . It tells us to tell each other right now that we love each other.” Leo Buscaglia

“Life asked Death, ‘Why do people love me, but hate you?’ Death responded, ‘Because you are a beautiful lie and I am a painful truth.” Author unknown

Made in the USA
Las Vegas, NV
11 January 2021